Recorder *from the* Beginning

POPS & SHOWS

John Pitts

Pops & Shows helps to increase the range of musical styles available to provide enjoyment for recorder players. The selection features some well-known tunes from the 'pop' field, both old and new, as well as highlights from Disney films and West End and Broadway showstoppers. Also included are some pop-folk items plus three exciting new pieces by John Pitts in rock, blues and boogie styles.

All the items are carefully arranged and graded so that the choice of key and systematic increase in the range of notes (pitches) will make the pieces accessible to as many players as possible. It is expected that players will have already reached the beginning of *Recorder from the Beginning Book 2*, in the author's widely popular teaching scheme. However, the desire to perform a particular piece will provide an incentive to learn any new note or rhythm involved, and personal choice and enjoyment are more likely to dictate the order of pieces played, rather than the order of new notes.

The Pupil's Book includes guitar chord symbols, and the Teacher's Book provides piano accompaniments for all the pieces.

In keeping with the 'repertoire' nature of the book, only a minimum of help or explanation is given. Where more help is required it is best to refer to the appropriate pages of the teaching scheme, *Recorder from the Beginning*.

Chester Music Limited
(A division of Music Sales Limited)
8/9 Frith Street, London W1V 5TZ

This book © Copyright 1999 Chester Music.
Order No. CH61540 ISBN 0-7119-7688-0

Music processed by Stave Origination.
Cover photography by Patrick Harrison.
Cover design by Jon Forss.
Printed in Great Britain by Printwise (Haverhill) Limited, Suffolk.

Contents

* Please note: this piece is in a different order in the Teacher's book to avoid a page turn.

Heartbeat

Words & Music by Bob Montgomery & Norman Petty
Arr. by John Pitts

On My Own
from *Les Misérables*

Music by Claude-Michel Schonberg, words by Herbert Kretzmer
Original Text by Alain Boublil & Jean-Marc Natel
Arr. by John Pitts

Can You Feel The Love Tonight

from Walt Disney Pictures' *The Lion King*

Music by Elton John, words by Tim Rice
Arr. by John Pitts

Another Day In Paradise

Words & Music by Phil Collins
Arr. by John Pitts

1. She calls out__ to the man__ on the street, __ 'Sir,__ can you help__ __ me?' 'It's cold__ and I've no - where to sleep, __ is there some - where_ you can tell____ me?'

1st time __ me?'

2nd & 3rd time

Yellow Submarine

Words & Music by John Lennon and Paul McCartney
Arr. by John Pitts

* In the Pupil's part, the music for verse 2 (bars 1 to 4) is written out in full, avoiding the repeat given in the piano part.
  The bar numbers here match the Pupil's part.

Scarborough Fair

Traditional
Arr. by John Pitts

The Floral Dance

Traditional
Arr. by John Pitts

Don't Cry For Me Argentina

from *Evita*

Music by Andrew Lloyd Webber, lyrics by Tim Rice
Arr. by John Pitts

Minty's Moody Blues

John Pitts

Morning Has Broken

Traditional
Arr. by John Pitts

Sloop John 'B'

Traditional arr. by John Pitts

(Everything I Do) I Do It For You

Words by Bryan Adams & Robert John 'Mutt' Lange
Music by Michael Kamen
Arr. by John Pitts

fight for you___ I'd lie___ for you,___ walk the wire for you,___ yeah_ I'd

die for___ you___ You know it's true, ev – ery – thing I

do, oh,_____ I do it for__ you.

Haley's Rock

John Pitts

* In the Pupil's Book the music is written in full avoiding the Da Capo used here.
  The bar numbers up to bar 28 match the Pupil's part.

Beauty And The Beast

from Walt Disney Pictures' *Beauty And The Beast*

Words by Howard Ashman, music by Alan Menken
Arr. by John Pitts

41

O Sole Mio

Music by Edorado di Capua, words by Giovanni Capurro
Arr. by John Pitts

House Of The Rising Sun

Traditional arr. by John Pitts

47

Peacherine Rag

Scott Joplin arr. John Pitts

49

* In the Pupil's part the music is written in full, avoiding the Dal Segno used here. The bar numbers up to bar 36 match the Pupil's part.

50

Boogie Rock

John Pitts

52

Brown Girl In The Ring

West Indian Traditional

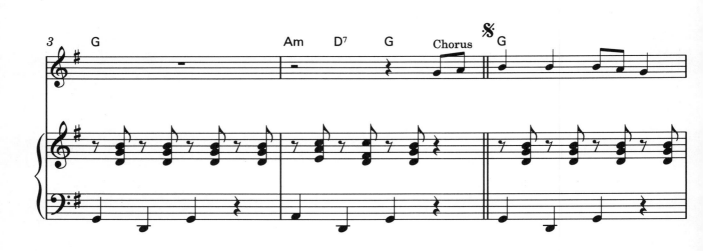

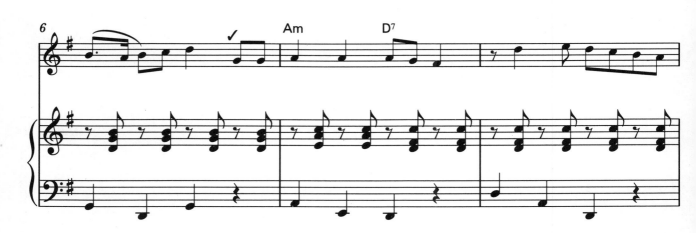

Recorder Duets *from the* Beginning

by John Pitts

Three collections of easy duets for descant recorders, complementing the author's popular teaching scheme *Recorder from the Beginning*.

These superb arrangements, ranging from Beethoven to the Blues, bring all the benefits and enjoyment of ensemble playing and are suitable for 2 players or class ensembles.

Precisely graded by level of difficulty of notes included.

Guitar chords are included, along with piano accompaniments and suggestions for additional percussion accompaniments.

Book 1 CH61213
Book 2 CH61214
Book 3 CH61215
Teacher's Book 1 CH61251
Teacher's Book 2 CH61252
Teacher's Book 3 CH61253

Descant & Treble Recorder Duets from the Beginning

At last, a great collection of duets for treble and descant! The interest is divided equally between the two parts, and both are precisely graded by level of difficulty and notes included.

Pupil's Book CH61297
Teacher's Book CH61304

Chester Music Limited
(A division of Music Sales Limited)
8/9 Frith Street, London W1V 5TZ